Origins

Cheeky Meeko

Cas Lester ✖ Jonatronix

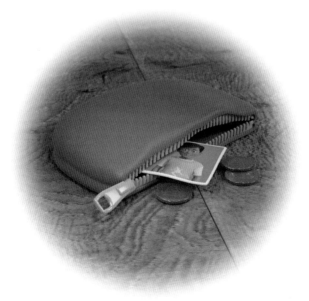

OXFORD

UNIVERSITY PRESS

Ant

Tiger

Ant's mum

Ant's dad

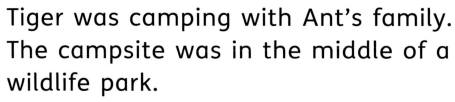

Tiger was camping with Ant's family. The campsite was in the middle of a wildlife park.

Suddenly, they heard a lion roaring.

Roooaaaarrr!

"I hope that lion can't get out!" said Mum.

"Yes, we don't want any wild animals in the tents!" joked Dad.

"Except for Tiger!" laughed Ant. Tiger grinned.

Just then, a cheeky monkey ran over. It grabbed Tiger's cap and raced off with it!

"Oo-oo-ooo!" it whooped. It sounded like the monkey was laughing at them!

The boys chased after the monkey, but a ranger soon caught it.

"I'm sorry. Meeko can be very cheeky," she laughed.

"Is Meeko your pet?" asked Ant.

"No, he lives in the wildlife park," she said.

When the boys got back to the tents, Mum gave Ant her purse. "Can you go to the shop to get some tomatoes for tea?" she asked.

The shop sold food and all sorts of camping stuff.

"Look. Popcorn!" cried Tiger. "Let's ask your mum if we can have a midnight feast!"

They went to pay the shopkeeper for the tomatoes. He was busy counting how many packets of crisps he had left. He looked worried.

"What's wrong?" asked Tiger.

"I think someone is stealing food from my shop," he said.

"That's terrible," said Ant.

When they got back to the tents they gave Mum her purse and the tomatoes.

"They sell popcorn in the shop," said Ant. "Can we have some for a midnight feast?"

"OK," she laughed. "I'll get some later!"

"Thanks!" cried the boys.

Bedtime came at last. Ant put the popcorn by the tent door. Tiger set his watch to wake them at midnight.

Just then, Mum popped her head in.
"Did you give me my purse back, Ant?" she asked. "I can't find it."

"I gave it to you with the tomatoes," said Ant.

"It must be here somewhere then," said Mum. "I'll keep looking."

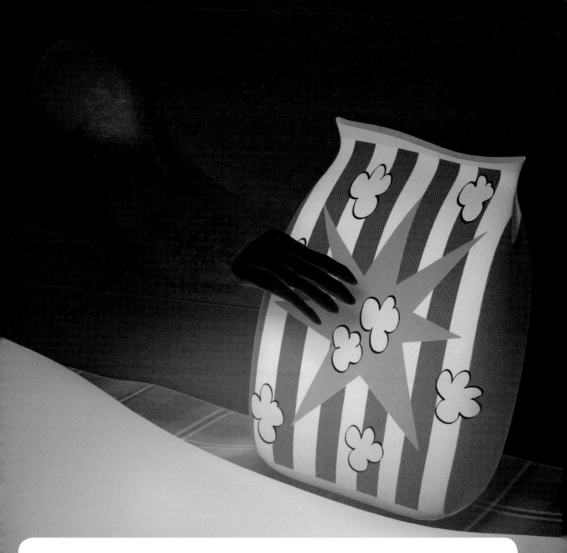

In the middle of the night, there was a sudden rustling noise. The boys woke up.

It was dark so Tiger switched on his torch. They saw someone stealing their midnight feast!

"Hey! Stop!" the boys cried, and rushed out of the tent. It was Meeko! He was running off with their food!

They chased after him, but he was too fast for them.

Just then, Ant saw something on the grass. It was shining in the moonlight.

"What's that?" he asked.

Tiger shone his torch on it. "It's a coin," he said.

A little further away they saw another coin, and then another one.

They followed the trail of shiny coins.
"It's like a moonlight treasure hunt!"
grinned Tiger.

"I wonder where it goes?" said Ant.

They soon found out. The coins led
them to the shop!

The shop was closed and it was dark inside. Tiger shone his torch through the window.

"Look! There's Meeko!" said Tiger. "He's eating our popcorn! Hey! Meeko!"

Then Tiger's torch flashed onto something with a shiny zip.

"That's Mum's purse!" cried Ant.
"Meeko must have taken it!"
    "Are you sure?" asked Tiger.
    "Let's go and check," said Ant.
    They turned the dials on their
watches and ...

They crawled through the letter slot and into the shop.

"It *is* Mum's purse!" cried Ant. "My photo is inside."

"The zip is open, so the money must have fallen out as Meeko ran along with it," said Tiger.

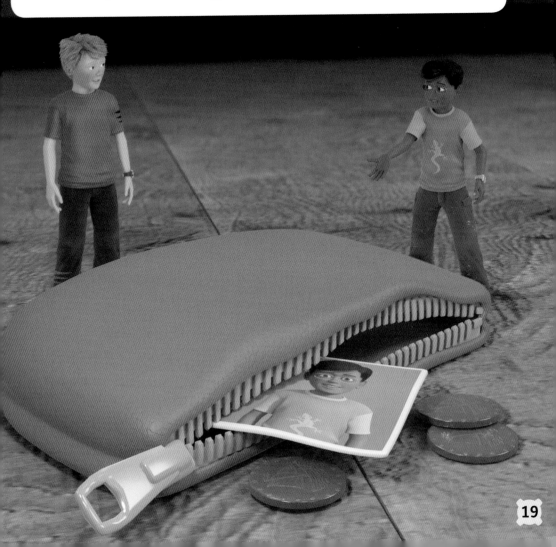

Then they spotted Meeko taking some crisps from the counter!
"It's Meeko who steals food from the shop!" said Tiger.

"Come on," said Ant. "We need to get back."

The two friends pushed the purse through the letter slot and climbed out after it. Then they turned the dials on their watches and grew back to normal size.

"I'll take a photo of Meeko so we can show the shopkeeper," said Ant, flipping up the camera on his watch.

"Switch your torch on, Tiger," said Ant. We can follow the coins back to the tent."

They picked up all the coins and put them back in Mum's purse as they went.

In the morning, Mum was thrilled to get her purse back. Ant and Tiger went to the shop. They showed the shopkeeper the picture of Meeko eating crisps.

"So it was the monkey stealing food!" he laughed. He gave them both an ice cream to say thank you.

Find out more ...

To find out about nocturnal animals read *Animals after Dark*

and read about Humphrey's nighttime adventure in *Danger in the Dark*.

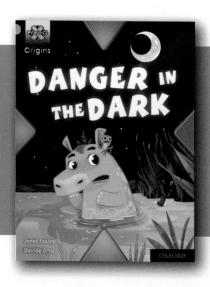